LESSON NUMBER 1

Read the *Introduction* and Chapter One *On Getting to Know Ourselves* and answer the following questions.

Question 1: What would knowing the fundamental law of life enable a person to do?

Question 2: What value would a knowledge of the fundamental law of life have for you personally?

Read Chapter Two *On the Laws of Survival and Abundance* **and answer the following questions.**

      Question 3: What is the only real guarantee of survival?

      Question 4: How could *you* apply this principle?

Read Chapter Three *On the Death of Consciousness* **and answer the following questions.**

Question 5: Describe Man's greatest weapon.

Question 6: Give a practical example of Man using this weapon to adapt his environment to him.

Question 7: How does awareness relate to consciousness?

Question 8: How does unconsciousness relate to death?

Student: Do not detach this strip

- -

SUPERVISOR'S GRADE

NAME   DATE

ADDRESS

CITY   STATE   ZIP CODE

PHONE/HOME   BUSINESS

E-MAIL   LESSON NUMBER 1

NAME	DATE
ADDRESS	
CITY	STATE ZIP CODE
PHONE/HOME	BUSINESS
E-MAIL	GRADE

LESSON NUMBER 2

Read Chapter Four *On Our Efforts for Immortality* and answer the following questions.

Question 9: Define *life* as an energy.

Question 10: What conquest is life engaged upon?

Question 11: Describe the two specific things that life must do in order to survive.

Question 12: How would procuring pleasure aid your survival?

Question 13: What is the function of the mind?

Question 14: Describe the mind's relationship to survival.

Question 15: What is meant by the "halfway point"?

Question 16: Are age and health criteria of this? Explain.

Student: Do not detach this strip

- -

LESSON NUMBER 3

Read Chapter Five *On Raising Our Level of Consciousness* and answer the following questions.

Question 17: Define pain.

Question 18: How is pain an automatic alarm system for a life organism? Give an example of this.

Question 19: What is "mental pain"?

Question 20: Give an example of mental pain.

Question 21: What does the accumulation of physical pain and loss bring about in an individual?

Question 22: What returns upon erasure of physical pain and loss?

Question 23: What can Dianetics do about pain and loss?

Question 24: Explain in your own words how restoring an individual's full consciousness restores his full potential.

- -

SUPERVISOR'S GRADE

NAME   DATE

ADDRESS

CITY   STATE   ZIP CODE

PHONE/HOME   BUSINESS

E-MAIL   LESSON NUMBER 3

LESSON NUMBER 4

Read Chapter Six *On Raising Our Level of Life and Behavior* **and answer the following questions.**

Question 25: What does the Tone Scale plot?

Question 26: Describe the vitality and consciousness of someone high on the Tone Scale.

Question 27: List the tones on the Tone Scale from 0.1 to 4.0.

Question 28: Describe someone moving up or down the Tone Scale in response to various situations encountered in life.

Question 29:   What are the chronic and acute aspects of the Tone Scale?

Question 30:   Give an example of chronic and acute tone level.

Question 31: What is the only mistake one can make in evaluating someone's level on the Tone Scale (Chart of Human Evaluation)?

Question 32: Explain how you would use the columns to find the tone level of a person.

Student: Do not detach this strip

- -

SUPERVISOR'S GRADE

NAME		DATE
ADDRESS		
CITY	STATE	ZIP CODE
PHONE/HOME	BUSINESS	
E-MAIL		

LESSON NUMBER 4

LESSON NUMBER 5

Read Chapter Seven *The Hubbard Chart of Human Evaluation* **and answer the following questions.**

Question 33: How can the position of a person on the Tone Scale vary?

Question 34: Give an example of someone you know and examine the chart to determine their chronic tone level. Now give an example of a time the person's tone varied from that chronic tone level.

Question 35: Define necessity level.

Question 36: Give an example of necessity level raising someone up the Tone Scale.

Question 37: How does the Tone Scale apply to groups?

Question 38: Describe the tone level of a group you have observed or been a part of.

Question 39: How does the state of one's possessions relate to different levels of the Tone Scale?

Question 40: What would you know about someone whose possessions were in excellent condition?

Student: Do not detach this strip

- -

SUPERVISOR'S GRADE

NAME   DATE

ADDRESS

CITY   STATE   ZIP CODE

PHONE/HOME   BUSINESS

E-MAIL   LESSON NUMBER 5

NAME		DATE	
ADDRESS			
CITY	STATE	ZIP CODE	
PHONE/HOME	BUSINESS		
E-MAIL			GRADE

LESSON NUMBER 6

Read Chapter Eight *Tone Scale Tests* and Chapter Nine *How to Use the Disk*. Answer the following questions for Chapter Nine.

Question 41: How is the disk used when recalling incidents?

Question 42: What should you eventually be able to do after continued use of the disk?

Question 43: What does a person do if he cannot at first get a recall of a sense perception?

Question 44: Give an example of when this rule would be applied.

Question 45: Define *Light Processing*.

Question 46: With *Self Analysis,* who is giving the reader Light Processing? Explain.

Question 47: Define *Deep Processing*.

Question 48: Who can deliver Deep Processing and why is that?

Student: Do not detach this strip

- -

SUPERVISOR'S GRADE

NAME		DATE	
ADDRESS			
CITY	STATE	ZIP CODE	
PHONE/HOME	BUSINESS		
E-MAIL			

LESSON NUMBER 6

Lesson Number 7

Read Chapter Ten *Processing Section* **and answer the following questions.**

> **Question 49:** What effect does the recall of *Self Analysis* questions have on *locks*?

> **Question 50:** Explain in your own words how the address to locks by *Self Analysis* questions renders engrams and secondaries.

Question 51: Give some of the perceptions through which one can contact the physical universe.

Question 52: What is the purpose of the disk with regard to perceptions?

Question 53: What is meant by *Repetitive Straightwire*?

Question 54: Give an example showing how Repetitive Straightwire is used and the end result.

Question 55: What is "boil-off"?

Question 56: Describe how one would handle boil-off when doing *Self Analysis* lists.

SUPERVISOR'S GRADE

NAME	DATE
ADDRESS	
CITY	STATE ZIP CODE
PHONE/HOME	BUSINESS
E-MAIL	

LESSON NUMBER 7

NAME		DATE	
ADDRESS			
CITY	STATE	ZIP CODE	
PHONE/HOME	BUSINESS		
E-MAIL			GRADE

LESSON NUMBER 8

Read List 1 *General Incidents* and answer the following questions.

Question 57: What is the purpose of the General Incidents list?

Question 58: What can the use of this list do for a person?

Read List 2 *Time Orientation* and answer the following questions.

Question 59: What is the "time track"?

Question 60: Are occlusions dangerous? Explain why.

Read List 3 *Orientation of Senses* **through the section** *Time Sense* **and answer the following questions.**

Question 61: Define the sense of *time*.

Question 62: Explain why clocks and calendars are artificial symbols representing time.

Read List 3 *Orientation of Senses*, **section** *Sight* **and answer the following questions.**

Question 63: Give the definition for the sense of *sight* and its subdivisions of *motion, color perception* and *depth perception.*

Question 64: Give an example of a profession that would require good perception of motion, color and depth.

Student: Do not detach this strip

- -

NAME		DATE	
ADDRESS			
CITY	STATE	ZIP CODE	
PHONE/HOME	BUSINESS		
E-MAIL			GRADE

LESSON NUMBER 9

Read List 3 *Orientation of Senses,* **section** *Relative Sizes* **and answer the following questions.**

Question 65: Define the sense of *relative size.*

Question 66: Make some comparisons to show relative size.

Read List 3 *Orientation of Senses,* **section** *Sound* **and answer the following questions.**

    Question 67: Define *sound.*

    Question 68: How can sound become associated with past pain? Explain.

Question 69: What are the different parts of sound?

Question 70: Give examples for each of these different parts of sound.

Read List 3 *Orientation of Senses,* **section** *Olfactory* **and answer the following questions.**

Question 71: What is the sense of *smell*?

Question 72: Give an example of unpleasant and pleasant smells.

Student: Do not detach this strip

- -

NAME		DATE
ADDRESS		
CITY	STATE	ZIP CODE
PHONE/HOME	BUSINESS	
E-MAIL		

LESSON NUMBER 9

LESSON NUMBER 10

Read List 3 *Orientation of Senses,* **section** *Touch* **and answer the following questions.**

Question 73: What is the sense of *touch*? Include its subdivisions.

Question 74: Explain in your own words why a sense of touch is very important.

Question 75: What is *anesthesia*?

Question 76: Give an example of anesthesia.

Read List 3 *Orientation of Senses,* section *Personal Emotion* and answer the following questions.

      Question 77: Define *mis-emotional.*

      Question 78: Describe a situation to which someone displayed mis-emotion. What was the rational emotion for that situation?

Question 79: What, in Dianetics, is a "control case"?

Question 80: How could you tell if a person was a "control case"?

Student: Do not detach this strip

- -

NAME	DATE
ADDRESS	
CITY	STATE	ZIP CODE
PHONE/HOME	BUSINESS
E-MAIL	

LESSON NUMBER 10

LESSON NUMBER 11

Read List 3 *Orientation of Senses*, section *Organic Sensation* and answer the following questions.

Question 81: Define the sense *organic sensation.*

Question 82: Give some examples of organic sensations.

Read List 3 *Orientation of Senses,* **section** *Motion Personal* **and answer the following questions.**

   Question 83: What is the perception of *personal motion?*

   Question 84: Give an example showing how some of the other perceptions assist in the perception of personal motion.

Read List 3 *Orientation of Senses,* section *Motion External* and answer the following questions.

      Question 85: How is *external motion* perceived?

      Question 86: Give an example of how external motion is perceived.

Read List 3 *Orientation of Senses,* **section** *Body Position* **and answer the following questions.**

Question 87: Describe how one can be aware of the *position of one's body* as a perception.

Question 88: Describe some body positions and how a person could perceive each of them.

Student: Do not detach this strip

- -

SUPERVISOR'S GRADE

NAME   DATE

ADDRESS

CITY   STATE   ZIP CODE

PHONE/HOME   BUSINESS

E-MAIL   LESSON NUMBER 11

LESSON NUMBER 12

Read List 4 *You and the Physical Universe* and answer the following questions.

Question 89: What is meant by the "adaptive" postulate or the "adjusted" postulate?

Question 90: On what does Man's success depend?

Question 91: What is the relationship between one's health and one's ability to handle the physical universe about one?

Question 92: Give an example where you have observed this relationship.

Question 93: What is *language*?

Question 94: Give an example you have seen of someone reacting to words as if they were physical force.

Question 95: What do all languages derive from?

Question 96: When answering the *Self Analysis* questions, explain why you do *not* want the time you were *told* to do something but instead want the time you performed the *action*.

SUPERVISOR'S GRADE

NAME		DATE	
ADDRESS			
CITY	STATE	ZIP CODE	
PHONE/HOME	BUSINESS		
E-MAIL			

LESSON NUMBER 12

LESSON NUMBER 13

Read List 5 *Assists to Remembering* **and answer the following questions.**

Question 97: How does one learn to "remember"?

Question 98: What could be said to account for poor memories?

Read List 6 *Forgetter Section* **and answer the following questions.**

Question 99: What action does the word "forget" rest on? Explain.

Question 100: Give an example of someone teaching another to forget something.

Read List 7 *Survival Factors* and answer the following questions.

   Question 101: What is meant by something being pro-survival or contra-survival?

   Question 102: Name some items that assist survival but could also inhibit survival.

Read List 8 *Imagination* and answer the following questions.

    Question 103: What is *imagination*?

    Question 104: Give an example of someone using their imagination to postulate a future goal.

Student: Do not detach this strip

LESSON NUMBER 14

Read List 9 *Valences* and answer the following questions.

Question 105: What is meant by being in one's own valence, compared to being out of one's own valence?

Question 106: How does being out of valence affect perceptions in recall?

Read List 10 *Interruptions* **and answer the following questions.**

Question 107: What can result from being *interrupted* in physical actions in early youth? Explain.

Question 108: Describe a time you saw someone interrupted in an action and what occurred.

Read List 11 *Invalidation Section* and answer the following questions.

    Question 109: Define *domination* and domination by *nullification.*

    Question 110: Give an example of someone using domination by nullification.

Question 111: What is "invalidation"?

Question 112: Describe some ways an individual can invalidate others.

- -

SUPERVISOR'S GRADE

NAME		DATE
ADDRESS		
CITY	STATE	ZIP CODE
PHONE/HOME	BUSINESS	
E-MAIL		

LESSON NUMBER 14

NAME		DATE	
ADDRESS			
CITY	STATE	ZIP CODE	
PHONE/HOME	BUSINESS		
E-MAIL			GRADE

LESSON NUMBER 15

Read List 12 *The Elements* **and the Special Session Lists** *If Recalling a Certain Thing Made You Uncomfortable.* **Answer the following questions on the Special Session Lists.**

Question 113: What are the three conditions you have lists for if recalling a certain thing makes you (or the person you are auditing) uncomfortable?

Question 114: Describe what you would do if you were running a *Self Analysis* list on another person and he or she indicated they wanted to avoid the recollection.

Question 115: Describe the beginning steps of the list that stabilizes *any* of the uncomfortable conditions.

Question 116: Give an example of a situation to which you would apply this list.

Question 117: According to medicine and experiment, how does vitamin B_1 and a heavy protein diet assist in processing?

Question 118: What are some of the things that are prevented by taking these while undergoing processing?

Read the Special Session Lists *End of Session List* **and answer the following questions.**

Question 119: What should you finish off a session of processing with?

Question 120: Describe the result you would achieve after running this list enough times at the end of a session.

- -

SUPERVISOR'S GRADE

NAME		DATE
ADDRESS		
CITY	STATE	ZIP CODE
PHONE/HOME	BUSINESS	
E-MAIL		

LESSON NUMBER 15